WORLDWIDE

Copyright © 2016 Claire Colston

The 'Clairey Fairy Tales' logo is a trademark of Fairy Worldwide Ltd.

Published in 2016 by
Fairy Worldwide Ltd
5 St Vincent Street
Edinburgh
EH3 6SW

www.fairyworldwide.com

British Library Cataloguing in Publication Data.
A catalogue record for this book is available from the British Library.

ISBN 978-0-9956985-0-5

Printed in Great Britain

For

Kai & Harrison
My Little Kings

&

Cora
My Little Queen

Cora's Dragons

Claire 'Fairy' Colston

www.claireyfairytales.com

My precious little child, please know, your whole life through

there are many little dragons that live inside of you

Each serve a special purpose, of this it is quite true

they are here to serve and honour, the special Being, that is You

When they know their special role, they rarely get upset

though if you have something new to do . . sometimes they forget

If dragons forget their special role, or their minds begin to doubt

They begin to feel a little scared . . and may panic, scream or shout

And though it doesn't feel too good, when they begin to shout and roar

When you feel them thumping on your heart, or making your tummy sore

We may just want to ignore our feelings and quash the hullabaloo

It's important to remember here, our dragons need help too.

So if you feel one kicking off, and you don't know what to do

Close your eyes and whisper inside . . "be still, I know what you can do"

Dont yell at them, or tell yourself off, for feeling whats inside

we do not want these dragons to run away or hide

We want to help them recognise and remember, why they're here

So we tell them "we can do this, you are safe, there is nothing to fear"

All dragons need when fear comes in, and their mind begins to doubt

Is a reminder that they're loved and safe, that you know what they're about

They can use their strength to help you stand up, and be strong

So you can do the job in hand, and you can move along

This is how you help them, when they start to kick a fuss

So they can use their fire and magic, to help you, be courageous

It's a very scary feeling, when they forget what they're here to do

and they know, they can do anything, when they feel loved by you.

So I want you to remember child, to know your whole life through

there are many little dragons that live inside of you

Each serve a special purpose, of this it is quite true
they are here to serve and honour
the special Being
That is . .

.. You

Clairey *Fairy* Tales

Claire 'Fairy' Colston is a Writer and Storytelling Consultant living just outside Edinburgh, Scotland with her two sons Kai & Harrison, and their little chocolate coloured ninja kitty, 'Fudgi'.

Fairy enjoys using the transformational, magical power of storytelling to help children and grown ups believe in their greatest self, building confidence and self esteem within.

Miss Fairy is no stranger to dragons, having met many of them over her lifetime, it took a little time for her to learn how to love them, though once she did, she found the strongest most powerful companions in all the world, they served in ways she never thought possible, and became her most treasured friends and allies.

For childrens resources, activity sheets or downloads please visit

www.claireyfairytales.com

WORLDWIDE

Publishers of heartfelt literature, programmes and material that
help children and grown ups believe in their greatest self,
building self confidence and self esteem within.

For more books and programmes on building self confidence for adults and children please visit

www.fairyworldwide.com

Creating a better world, by telling better stories.

Thank you for supporting our mission.